Contents

A safe place
Focus on: a_e as in m*a*k*e* 3

Kate bakes a cake
Focus on: a_e, ai, ay
as in m*a*k*e*, as in r*ai*n, s*ay* 10

Kane's tail!
Focus on: ai, ay as in r*ai*n, s*ay* 18

Phonemes: ch, sh, th, wh, ph, a_e, ai, ay
'Tricky' words: my, can't, does, love

About this book

These short stories are designed to give children blending and reading practice. They are decodable, which means the words in them only include letter shapes and sounds that the children have learned. The stories gradually introduce 'tricky' words, building on the learning in the Red Series.

The progression links directly to the teaching order in the Letterland teaching range. Each story begins with a title page that provides important information for children and teachers.

Story title

Focus on: New spelling patterns introduced

New 'tricky' words: Common words with irregular spellings

Basic teaching tips:

- Encourage the sounding out of decodable words (and any decodable parts of 'tricky' words).
- Discuss the stories with the children to ensure comprehension and engagement.
- Encourage re-reading in pairs or individually to develop fluency and reading for meaning.

Red Series introduces the a-z letters and sounds and some 'tricky words'. On completion of this series, the following words remain tricky in part: a, the, she, oh, for, that, ok, they, says, her, this, to, said, of, what, you, was, want, come, sees, asks, do. These words are included in **Blue Series**.

A safe place

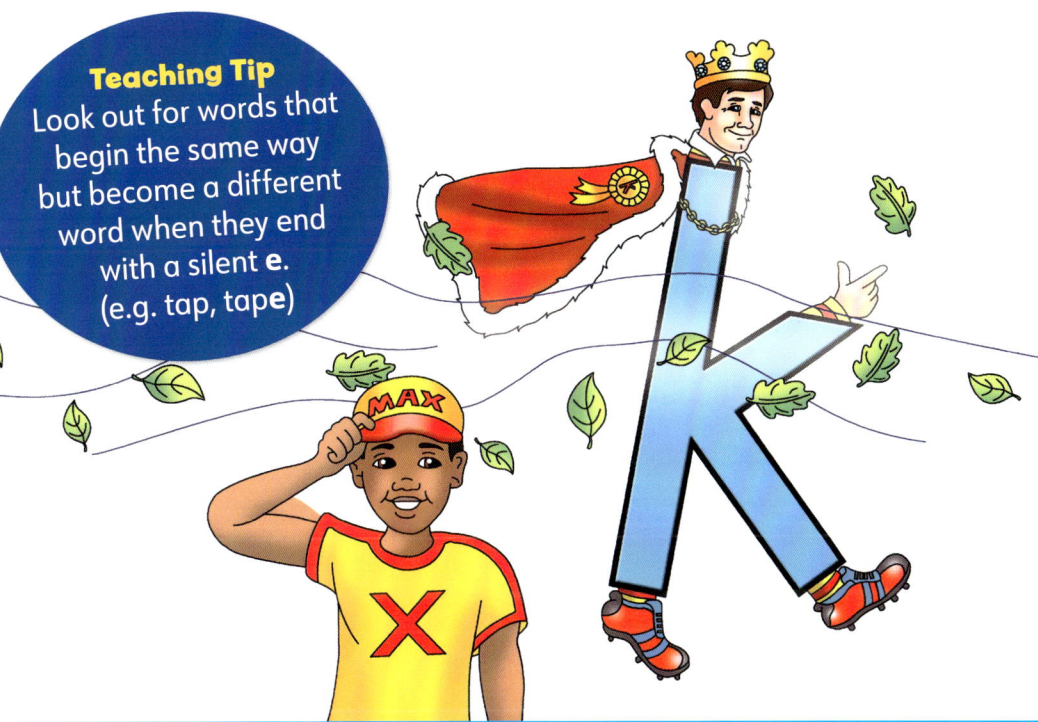

Teaching Tip
Look out for words that begin the same way but become a different word when they end with a silent **e**.
(e.g. tap, tap**e**)

Focus on: a_e as in *m*a*k*e

The wind is strong! It can lift up Fix-it Max's cap and flip up Kicking King's cape.

The wind is strong! It takes the Hat Man's hat. He hates it when the wind takes his hat.

The wind is strong! The pup had a plan to get up in a plane. He cannot do that.

The wind is strong! It is a gale.
They must find a place that is safe!

The pup has a plan. "Tap on that and tape that up!"

The wind is strong! It is a gale.
But this is a safe place!

Kate bakes a cake

Tricky word: can't

Focus on: a_e, ai, ay
as in m<u>a</u>k<u>e</u>, r<u>ai</u>n, s<u>ay</u>

Kate wants to bake a cake for her Mum. But she has no eggs.

They go to the shops. Kate gets the things to make the cake.

They get back to the kitchen.
Kane, the dog, is glad to see them.

Kane has a sniff of the cake. Dad says, "Get off, Kane! He can't stay in the kitchen!"

Dad went off to play a game of chase with Kane. Kate put red grapes on top of the cake.

Mum and Dad came in.
"I made this cake for you, Mum," says Kate. "Kane! You must wait!"

"Thank you, Kate. The cake you made is fantastic!" Mum says. "I can't wait!"

Kane's tail!

Tricky words: love, does

Focus on: ai, ay as in *rain*, *say*

I have got a dog with a plain chain on his neck. His name is on the tag.
His name is Kane. He wags his tail.

Kane yaps. He yaps at the mail man. He yaps at the train. He yaps at the rain. Then he wags his tail.

When I say, "Sit," he stands up. When I say, "Stay," he does not wait. He runs off. Then he wags his tail.

He jumps in the lake, then shakes himself and gets me wet! Then he wags his tail. I love my dog, Kane.

About this series

This series of 10 books accompanies the Letterland teaching range. Each book contains a selection of short stories. In total there are 32 engaging stories featuring the phonic elements listed below as well as some 'tricky' high-frequency words.

Book	Focus elements	As in the word...	Story titles
1	sh, ch, th, th, wh, ph	chip, shop, that, thing	Check on the chicks Shep and me What is that thing?
2	a_e, ai, ay	make, rain, say,	A safe place Kate bakes a cake Kane's tail!
3	e_e, ea, ee, y	these, sea, bee, baby	A trip to the sea Mr E's trees Happy!
4	i_e, ie, igh, y	like, tie, night, my	Ben rides his bike Cats at night What a mess!
5	o_e, oa, ow	home, boat, show	The bad goat When the cold wind blows Lost in the Queen's maze
6	u_e, ue, oo, ew	cube, blue, moon, few, grew	Stuck on a dune A day at the zoo The Hat Man's new roof
7	ar, or, er, ir, ur, wr	farm, for, her, girl, fur, write	The big match Snapshots The bird girls My very bad morning
8	o, oo, u, oy, oi	son, book, put, boy, coin	Oscar's brother The big pull Nick's noisy new toy
9	aw, au, ow, ou	saw, cause, how, out,	Draw it! The house mouse Look now!
10	Review ear, air	pear, year, fair	My shark dream A fresh feast Bears at the fair A fairy story

Collect the sets

Phonics Readers - Red Series

Phonics Readers - Blue Series

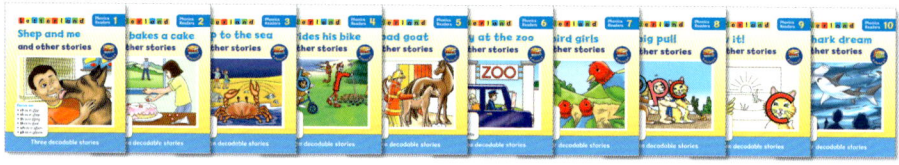

Published by Letterland International Ltd. 8/10 South Street, Epsom, Surrey, KT18 7PF, UK.
www.letterland.com
ISBN: 978-1-78248-181-2
Product Code: TJ03

© Letterland International 2016
LETTERLAND™ is a trademark of Letterland International Ltd.

First published 2013. This new edition published 2016.
Reprinted 2023.
10 9 8 7 6 5 4 3 2

Authors: Stamey Carter and Lisa Holt
Originator of Letterland: Lyn Wendon
Artwork: Doreen Shaw
Design: Lisa Holt

The author asserts the moral right to be identified as the author of this work. All rights reserved. No part of this publication may be reproduced, stored in a retrieval system, or transmitted in any form or by any means, electronic, mechanical, photocopying, recording or otherwise, without either the prior permission of the Publisher or a licence permitting restricted copying in the United Kingdom issued by the Copyright Licensing Agency Ltd, 90 Tottenham Court Road, London W1T 4LP. This book is sold subject to the condition that it shall not be by way of trade or otherwise be lent, hired out or otherwise circulated without the Publisher's prior consent.

Printed in Beirut, Lebanon.